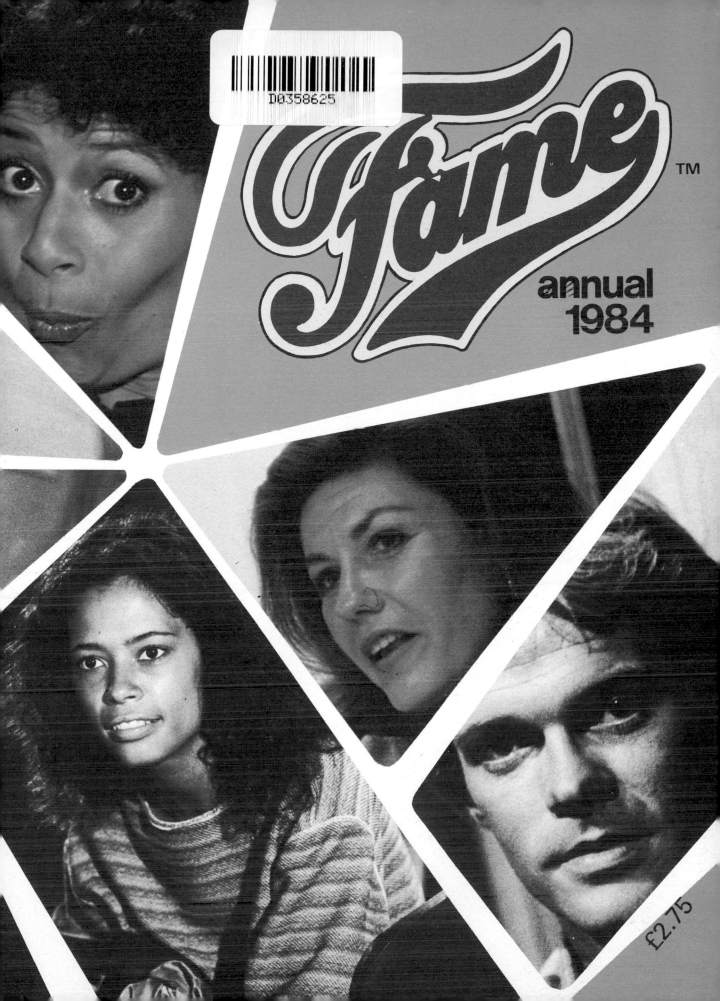

Fame ™

annual 1984

£2.75

Contents

Copyright © MCMLXXXIII by Metro-Goldwyn-Mayer Film Co.
All rights reserved throughout the world.
Published in Great Britain by
World International Publishing Limited.
A Pentos Company,
P.O. Box 111, Great Ducie Street, Manchester M60 3BL.
Printed in Great Britain by Collins, Glasgow.
SBN 7235 6683 6.

Lori Singer is Julie Miller

Lori Singer is one of those lucky people with a talent for doing all the things they turn their hand to very well! The daughter of famous conductor Jacques Singer, Lori is herself an excellent cellist, has had a successful modelling career, and is now turning her considerable talents to acting — as we can see in *Fame*.

Julie Miller, the character Lori plays, is a newcomer to New York, and takes a little time to settle into her new environment, although with a little help from her new friends she seems to be doing just fine! Basically a shy, quiet person, Julie needs to build her self-confidence in order to achieve the fame she deserves — and with friends like the ones in *Fame*, who can doubt that she will?

DEDICATED TO THE ONE...

Angelo Martelli sat behind the wheel of his taxi and watched his son climb the front steps of The School of the Arts and greet his fellow pupils with a cheery wave. Angelo smiled. He had been worried about Bruno of late. Professor Shorofsky had set a homework assignment – something about interpreting one of the classics on a modern instrument – and the young musician was becoming far too involved with it. He had taken to locking himself away for hours on end, searching for the perfection that only he felt was necessary, and it was starting to depress him.

That was Bruno's trouble – Angelo thought – everything had to be just right. But this morning, as Angelo watched Bruno laugh and joke with Doris, Danny and the others, he knew that his son had pushed the assignment to the back of his mind – for a few hours at least. That was good.

As he waved goodbye and pulled away from the side-walk, Angelo switched on one of his son's tapes and began to sing along. Today was going to be an enjoyable day, he decided.

The streets of New York roared with the usual ridiculous amount of traffic. Cars, buses and juggernauts poured out of side streets and into the main flows with little regard for courtesy or safety. Horns blared deafeningly as early morning pedestrians cautiously or suicidally negotiated the concrete canyons in their daily dash to work. Lights and traffic control monitors flicked on and off with ludicrous rapidity. Tempers began to flare.

And in the middle of it all, taking everything in his stride, Angelo Martelli picked up his first fare of the day.

"761 East Seventy Fourth," the business type declared.

"Right." Angelo clicked on his meter and pulled out into the lane.

"This is one busy city," the business type yelled over the sound of Bruno's tape. "I don't know how you guys can stand driving around it all day. I suppose the music helps."

"My son," Angelo called back. "He recorded it."

"Really?" the business type said, bending forward. "My son's in a band, y'know. Back in Oregon. That's where I hail from. Now *there's* a place where —"

From that moment on Angelo knew that he shouldn't have opened his mouth. There were just some fares who you didn't start a conversation with. They were the talkers. Angelo had seen them before, on their way to important meetings, going on and on about anything that would take their minds off whatever fate awaited them, dragging drivers into idle chatter as if the taxi cruised along on auto-pilot. There was nothing you could do but nod and throw in the odd comment, that and keep your eyes on the road. You usually got by okay.

But this morning was different. This morning there was a third party involved — an out-of-town driver, a lemming, a guy who thought he owned the road and acted as if he did.

The caravanette pulled out right in front of Angelo just as he had

turned to throw in an occasional understanding nod to his fare. He turned back just as his taxi came within a few seconds of impact with the other vehicle. Angelo jumped in his seat, slammed on the brakes and spun the steering wheel hard to the left. But it was too late. The taxi slammed sideways into the caravanette and rebounded into the centre lane. Angelo fought for control but the taxi was already well on its careering path of destruction. It spun to face the wrong way up the centre lane, collided with two cars, and was hurled backwards into the nose of the caravanette. The last thing that Angelo was aware of was the sound of buckling metal. Then his world exploded . . .

The atmosphere in Professor Shorofsky's classroom was tense. All eyes were on Bruno Martelli as he squirmed in his seat behind the piano. For the third day running Shorofsky had asked Bruno to present his homework assignment to the class, and for the third day running Bruno sat in embarrassed silence.

Shorofsky walked slowly over to the piano and frowned. Bruno squirmed some more. It was amazing how much of an aura of threat the old music teacher could radiate with that one little expression.

"I trust," Shorofsky said, "that your sudden inability to utter coherent sounds once again indicates that your assignment is incomplete. Would you care to tell me why?"

involved in a collision. The hospital notified us a few minutes ago."

Bruno said nothing for a few seconds then stared blankly into space. "Hospital?"

Elizabeth nodded. There was no point in beating around the bush with Bruno. He was too intelligent for that. "It's serious, I'm afraid. Your father's in intensive care."

Bruno took a deep breath and looked at Elizabeth. " Can I see him?"

Elizabeth placed her hand on Bruno's arm. She could feel him shaking. "Of course. We'll go right away."

Bruno and Elizabeth arrived at the hospital twenty minutes later. A young nurse escorted them between the rows of easy-observation glass panels that made up the intensive care ward and into the booth occupied by Angelo Martelli. The nurse stood unobtrusively in a corner while Bruno and Elizabeth approached the bed. "I can only give you two minutes," she said.

Angelo lay immobile under a crisp white sheet. His eyes were closed. All around the bed were the banks of complex monitors and life-support systems that were necessary to sustain life in a body that was temporarily unable to do

"I'm – er – not happy with it yet," Bruno said weakly. "Some parts still don't feel right."

"Some parts still don't feel right," Shorofsky repeated. "I see." Shorofsky pulled himself up to his full height and let out a deep breath. "Mr Martelli. Much as I admire your unflagging search for perfection in all things musical, I must point out that such creative freedom is normally reserved for those who have attained a position of eminence in their chosen field and not for those whose span of years on this earth is generally less than most of the instruments in this classroom. Do I make myself clear?"

Bruno swallowed, oblivious to the giggles from his classmates.

"Yes, Sir, you do."

"Good. Then I expect –"

Shorofsky trailed off as Elizabeth Sherwood appeared in the classroom doorway and beckoned his attention. "Professor," she said, "could I have a word with Bruno Martelli? Outside."

Shorofsky was about to say something about it being highly irregular, but he thought better of it when he saw the expression on the english teacher's face. He nodded and motioned Bruno to the door.

"I'll talk to you about it later," Elizabeth said to Shorofsky as she closed the door.

Elizabeth ushered Bruno to a quiet part of the corridor and sat him down. Bruno knew instinctively that something was wrong. "What is it? What's happened?"

Elizabeth sat down next to him. "Your father. There's been an accident . . ." She waited a few seconds while the news sank in and then continued. "His taxi was

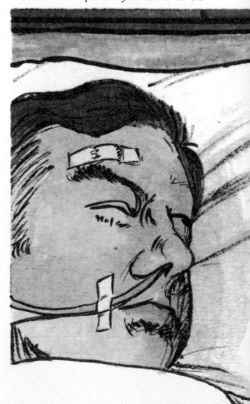

so for itself. Bruno stood stock-still, staring down at his father. The only movement in the room was on the screens of the ECG and EEG machines that were positioned above the bed. The green blips moved slowly but steadily across the illuminated lattice graph.

"Pop," Bruno whispered. "Hey, Pop."

Elizabeth put her arm around Bruno's shoulder. "He can't hear you, Bruno. The doctors say he's been in a coma since arrival."

Bruno let his hand move up to the intravenous drip bottle that hung suspended from a stand beside the bed. He traced his fingers down the feed-tube and let them gently rest on his father's arm. "He's all I've got, you know."

Elizabeth smiled. "I know." She pulled Bruno towards her until his head was cradled on her shoulder. The nurse discreetly signalled that their time was almost up. Elizabeth nodded. "We have to go," she said gently.

The journey away from the hospital was a silent one. Bruno had protested when the time to leave came, saying that he wanted to stay with his father, but Elizabeth and the nurse had eventually persuaded him that he could be of no help and would only have been in the way. Bruno had finally agreed to let Elizabeth drive him home.

"Are you going to be okay?" she asked as she dropped him off at the Martelli house.

Bruno nodded and opened the front door. "Thanks for your help, Miss Sherwood."

"Will we see you in school

tomorrow? It might be for the best. Take your mind off things . . ."

But Bruno was already half-hidden behind the door, already lost in this own thoughts. "No," he said as he closed the door all the way. "No, I don't think so."

The School of the Arts was as hectic as usual the following day. Elizabeth was plunged into a series of classes that she had been dreading but which actually turned out to be quite enjoyable. Only one thing marred an excellent debating session on the classics versus modern literature – the conspicuous absence of Bruno Martelli. Elizabeth found herself continually glancing at his empty seat and realised that she was more concerned about his welfare than she had first thought. It was that realisation that caused

It was dark by the time Professor Shorofsky arrived at the Martelli house. There were no lights on inside the house and no one answered the door when Shorofsky rang. The old man shivered in the cold night air and rapped hard on the door itself. It swung open before him.

The house seemed to be deserted. Shorofsky moved through the dark, cold rooms searching for a light switch. He had just located one when he spotted a thin line of light filtering out under a door at the base of the stairs.

Shorofsky opened it. A flight of steps led down into the basement... Shorofsky negotiated the steps to find Bruno sitting in an old chair in the corner of the basement. A crumpled bag of half-eaten potato chips lay beside him. He looked as if he hadn't slept since Elizabeth had left the previous day.

Shorofsky sighed and perched himself on the edge of a table. Bruno did not seem aware of his presence.

"Shorofsky does not journey three-quarters of the way across town to be ignored," the old man said suddenly.

Bruno started, suddenly aware that he was no longer alone. "Professor, what –?"

"I came to find out how your father is," Shorofsky went on. "I expected answers from Bruno Martelli, not a living corpse."

"His – er – his condition is unchanged," Bruno said falteringly. He straightened himself up in the chair. "I've been calling every hour."

"Ah," Shorofsky declared. "And

her to speak with Professor Shorofsky after class...

"You want *me* to visit the boy?" Shorofsky queried.

Elizabeth nodded. "You know Bruno as well as I do, Professor. You know how introspective he can be. If we leave him alone at a time like this, all sorts of things will start going through his mind. He needs to be kept busy – and I think that you're one of the few people who can get that through to him."

"I would not rely on this old man too much if I were you," Shorofsky sighed, "but I will try."

"Thank you," Elizabeth called after Shorofsky as he disappeared up the corridor.

"No need, no need," Shorofsky muttered to himself. "I care about him too, you know."

what have you been doing between hours, may I ask?"

Bruno shrugged noncommitally. "Sitting . . . thinking . . ."

"Sitting and thinking," Shorofsky repeated. He pointed to the bag of potato chips. "And starving yourself half to death by the looks of things."

"Professor, I don't understand what you want . . ."

Shorofsky slid down off the table and moved over to Bruno's synthesiser. He picked a sheet of music off the top. "I want you to keep yourself occupied, take your mind off things. Do you not think that one Martelli in hospital is enough?" He dropped the music in Bruno's lap. "Play me something."

"Professor, I really don't feel like —"

Shorofsky held up his hand. "Look at yourself, boy. How do you think your father would feel if he could see you now?" He gestured towards the synthesiser. "Play me some music," he said gently.

Bruno strode reluctantly up to the synthesiser and sighed. He switched it on and began to play. Shorofsky settled down in the chair. The music that flowed through the basement was that of Bruno's homework assignment, an electronic reworking of a classical medley. As Shorofsky listened he realised just how much talent Bruno really had — the boy had magically transformed a standard piece into something *personal*.

Shorofsky smiled, the music conjuring feelings that he had thought long forgotten. He was strangely disappointed when the music trailed off.

"That's as far as I've managed to get," Bruno said. "I don't think I'll be able to finish it now that my father —" Bruno stood up. "It just doesn't feel right any more."

Shorofsky lifted himself out of the chair and walked to the synthesiser. Without saying a word he sat in front of the keyboard and began to play a piece of his own music. Bruno felt his throat tighten as the melancholic strains surrounded him. When Shorofsky had finished he sat for a few seconds in silence and then turned to face Bruno.

"I composed that piece soon

after fleeing Nazi Germany," he said. "I had left behind all that was dear to me and was alone for the first time in my life." Shorofsky stood up and walked to Bruno. "I knew that I would never see my family again."

Bruno saw the pain in the old man's eyes and felt his heartache as acutely as his own. "How could you work at a time like that?"

Shorofsky smiled wistfully. "Because music is the greatest tool for expression in this world," he said. Shorofsky picked up the music sheet containing the unfinished homework assignment and thrust it at Bruno. "Don't betray yourself or your father," he added. "Put down what you *feel*."

Bruno said nothing as he took the sheet and stared at it. Shorof-sky walked slowly towards the steps. "I expect to hear it when it is finished," he said, as he started to climb.

Bruno appeared at The School of the Arts in the afternoon of the following day. Shorofsky had just finished ushering out a class full of pupils when the young musician appeared in the doorway.

Shorofsky smiled. "Is it done?" he asked.

Bruno walked into the room and slid a cassette into the small tape deck that Shorofsky always kept on hand. He pressed the play button and stepped back as his composition poured out of the speakers.

Shorofsky sat in silence throughout the five minutes that the recording lasted. "You have created something to be proud of," he declared when it had finished.

"I only wish my father could hear it," Bruno said as he ejected the tape. "All the work I've put into it just seems futile while he's lying there like that."

Shorofsky stroked his beard, an idea forming. "Maybe," he said slowly, "maybe he can." He picked up his papers from his desk and moved towards the door. "Go home now," he said to Bruno. "I'll call you."

Bruno received the call from Shorofsky two hours later. The old music teacher was at the hospital and he wanted Bruno to join him as soon as possible. He stipulated that he must bring the tape. Bruno made his way there to find Shorof-

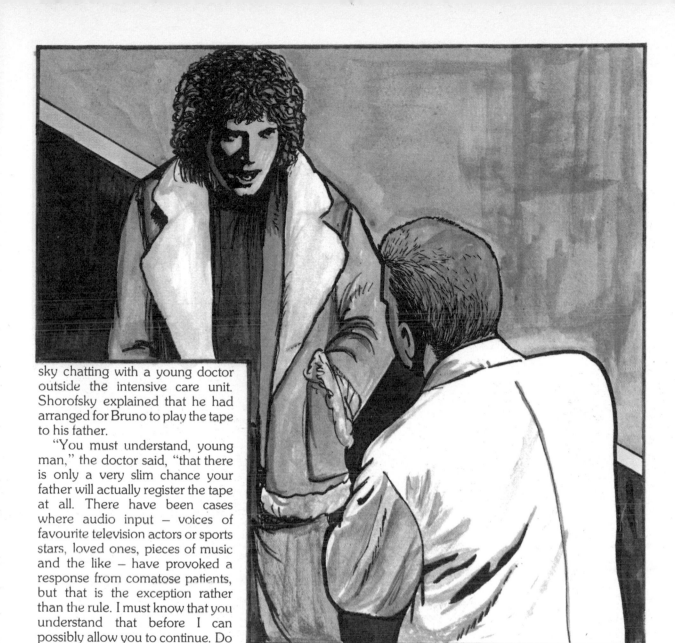

sky chatting with a young doctor outside the intensive care unit. Shorofsky explained that he had arranged for Bruno to play the tape to his father.

"You must understand, young man," the doctor said, "that there is only a very slim chance your father will actually register the tape at all. There have been cases where audio input – voices of favourite television actors or sports stars, loved ones, pieces of music and the like – have provoked a response from comatose patients, but that is the exception rather than the rule. I must know that you understand that before I can possibly allow you to continue. Do you understand?"

Bruno nodded. "Even if it doesn't work," he said, "at least I'll have tried."

"Very well," the doctor said. He motioned Bruno and Shorofsky through the door into intensive care.

Angelo Martelli lay in exactly the same position he had when Bruno had last visited. Although his body was now healthy once more, his mind was still trapped in the dark limbo that existed somewhere far below the surface. There was no reaction as the doctor slipped a pair of earphones over his head and signalled for Bruno to give him the tape. Bruno did so and stepped back to stand with Shorofsky.

"The tape is now playing," the doctor said.

No sound filtered out through the tightly clamped earphones and Bruno, Shorofsky and the doctor waited in tense silence while it played through once, then twice, then three times.

Bruno felt as if every second lasted an hour. The expressions of Shorofsky and the doctor reflected his own feeling of failure. The tape wasn't getting through to Angelo.

The doctor sighed and shook his head. "It's no use," he said. Slowly he moved to disconnect the tape machine.

"Wait!" Bruno cried. "Look!"

Bruno pointed to Angelo's arm.

Muscles were gently flexing beneath the surface of the skin. As the three watched, the flexing continued down the arm until one of Angelo's fingers lifted almost imperceptibly from the sheet.

Shorofsky and the doctor looked at one another in congratulatory fashion before the doctor moved to the bedside and began checking Angelo's pulse and respiration. He smiled at Bruno. "Your father is on his way back," he said. "The tape worked."

But Bruno wasn't listening. He too was now by the bedside, clutching his father's hand and waiting. Waiting for the moment when he opened his eyes . . .

13

Carol Mayo Jenkins is Elizabeth Sherwood

Sometimes regarded as a bit of a dragon in the classroom, Elizabeth Sherwood is one of those teachers who manages to bring out the best in her students — by being a dragon! In the past she has had many confrontations with her students — particularly with Leroy, but although sometimes they may resent being pushed into working, they know that if ever they are in difficulties Elizabeth will always do her best to help and give them her full support.

Carol Mayo Jenkins, who plays Elizabeth in *Fame*, reflects some of the character's desire for success in her life as an actress. She is one of those determined and versatile actresses who rarely finds herself out of work, and has played parts with astounding success, from the classics to contemporary drama. For her, as for the rest of the cast of *Fame*, the show is extremely rewarding and energetic — and Carol Mayo Jenkins certainly puts all her talents to very good use as Elizabeth Sherwood!

FUNNY TURN

"Fame is a food that dead men eat, I have no stomach for such meat."

Miss Sherwood finished writing the quotation on the board and turned to face her class. She noticed Danny Amatullo drawing something on the palm of his hand.

"Do you know who wrote that, Mr Amatullo?" she asked.

"You did," answered Danny, covering his mouth and raising his hand in the traditional Hollywood Indian greeting. There was an octopus drawn on it. He waggled his fingers and swivelled in his seat so the rest of the class could see the tentacles come to life.

"This is an old wave joke," he explained, waggling some more, "glove puppets without gloves." Miss Sherwood waited until the groans died down, and then read out the quotation once again.

"It was written by Henry Austin Dobson," she said.

"Never heard of him."

"And because, Mr Amatullo, in that vast repository of information you call a brain, there is no entry under Henry Austin Dobson, then of course the man had absolutely nothing worth saying."

"I'm sorry, Miss Sherwood," said Danny, stung by the edge in her voice, "but that sounds like the kind of stuff they used to write before television was invented. This is 1984 – the modern world. We've got aeroplanes now, rockets in space, computers, nuclear stuff, Dudley Moore. I don't think we should be spending so much time on what some guy dreamed up when he was painting his body with mud. That stuff is just history."

"And history is of no value at all?"

"History is a lot of dead people running round in silly clothes."

"You disagree that people who don't learn from history are forced to repeat it?"

"I don't know –" Danny was beginning to feel uneasy.

"And that the second time round, tragedy becomes hideous farce?"

"I'm sure you're right, Miss Sherwood," said Danny, his hands flat on the desk, "I can't fight what's coming down. I want to be a comic, not a – a –"

"Fool?" suggested Doris.

Miss Sherwood smiled.

"Don't you see, Danny," she said, "a knowledge of tragedy is essential to someone trying to learn comedy?"

Danny slumped back further in his chair and slipped the hand with the octopus on into his pocket.

"The way I see it, Miss Sherwood," he said, "is that you've got two people in a stream, fighting with swords – right? The hero is in trouble. He takes a shot at the other guy and misses. His sword breaks. That's tragedy. In comedy his sword doesn't shatter – it bends, it stays bent and more likely than not it ends up with a fish stuck on the end of it."

"You've got a vivid imagination, Mr Amatullo."

"Yeah," interrupted Doris, "he thinks he's funny."

The lunch bell rang and Miss Sherwood dismissed the class. As Danny sidled out she called him over.

"I was wrong," he said, holding his hands up in apology. Miss Sherwood stifled a smile at the sight of the octopus. "I don't mean to be any trouble. I've just got a low threshold of knowledge."

"You don't think you've got anything to learn from the accumulated knowledge of thousands of years of recorded history?"

"I'd rather have ten minutes with Bob Hope."

"It's the things you find difficult that you must concentrate on, if you're ever going to learn. So from now on – no more clowning in class, right?"

Danny shrugged.

"Right?" repeated Miss Sherwood, more forcefully.

"Right," said Danny, turning to go.

"Oh, Danny?" said Miss Sherwood. Danny turned. "I did find your theories on humour quite succinct." Danny smiled.

"That's a funny thing about humour," he said, "you never know how it's going to go down. You can tell a joke in New York that has the crowds roaring, and yet in L.A. that same joke won't even raise a smile."

"Why's that, Danny?"

"They can't hear it."

Danny wandered into the lunch room. Four girls, including Coco, were singing an accappella version of *God Bless America* in one corner, hands cupped to their ears, eyes almost closed in concentration. Leroy stood nearby, his face expressionless as he listened to the animated talk of a track-suited young man wearing a gold, red and green hat. Bruno, Doris and Julie sat at a table swapping sandwiches.

Danny slid through the crowds and sat down with them. Doris pulled a copy of *Backstage* from her bag and held it up to her face. Julie turned her attention to a tuna fish sandwich. Bruno gazed across the crowded room with a glazed look in his eye, his fingers drumming idly on a chocolate bar as his mind wove rhythms through the currents of conversation.

Danny clapped his hands behind his head and sat back in his chair. "It's tough at the top all right," he offered.

He leaned across the table towards Doris. She moved the paper higher in front of her face.

"Is it true you were a bottle baby, Doris?" he asked.

Doris gritted her teeth, waiting for the punchline. It never came. She peered round the side of her

paper with one eye. Danny was reading a small article at the foot of the page.

Doris immediately turned the page around. It was a short piece about a 'well known producer' in town to see a comedy revue.

But Danny had already seen enough. His mind was racing. A comedy revue . . . by invitation only: to Danny that meant one thing only. They were going to film it. Visions of Richard Pryor, John Landis, Mel Brooks! He had to get in there.

The theatre was a drab building, sort of off off-Broadway, and when Danny arrived there after school his spirits sank a little. A group of grizzled, weatherbeaten old men in thick coats passed a brown paper bag among themselves on the corner. The doors were locked, but it was still early. Danny comforted

himself with the thought that they were probably setting everything up inside.

"Hey, you!"

Danny turned to the sound. A girl of about fourteen years of age was walking towards him, fast. She had blue hair and wore a black leather jacket, a thick studded black belt and white hot-pants.

"Me?" asked Danny.

"Yeah you – scram!"

"What?"

"Get out of here," spat the girl. Small as Danny was, she only came up to his chest.

"This is my patch. Quit crowding my action. Any stuff that gets sold round here – I sell it – right?"

"Hey," protested Danny, "I don't want to sell anything."

"You're not going to," said the girl. "The customers want something – I got it. Popcorn, peanuts,

ice cream, beer –"

"Aren't you a little young to be selling beer?" asked Danny.

"Look behind you, boy."

Danny turned. At the kerb, leaning against a black '68 Cadillac packed with bottles and bright-coloured bags was a man with arms so wide it looked like he had grapefruits sewn under his skin.

Danny walked past the men on the corner and turned down an alleyway, certain that there must be another way in. He tried the back door. It was locked. He looked at the wall. About ten feet above him a small grille was hanging by one screw. The hole it was meant to cover was just about big enough for him to squeeze through. "Come on, Amatullo," he said, dragging a garbage can under the hole, "you knew it wasn't going to be easy when you set out."

Danny climbed on the garbage can and reached up to the hole. The sides were lined with grime and his left hand landed on something wet. Danny turned off his imagination and hauled himself up.

The hole was smaller than he had thought, but he managed to get his head through. Inside, the room was dim, quiet, dusty. There was a sink in the corner and the floor was littered with empty crates. Stacked against one wall were some cardboard boxes stamped FRAGILE.

Danny squeezed his right arm through, and then his left. He was beginning to wriggle forward when the door of the room opened. A squat, curly-haired man came in. He wore skin-tight satin trousers and a bright red shirt open to the waist. He washed his hands, combed his hair, then sat down on one of the crates and lit a cigarette. Danny stared down at the back of his head and tried to move silently backwards. He couldn't.

He was stuck. He pushed and he pulled but he couldn't move. He was wondering whether to ask the curly-haired man to help when he heard a sound from behind him and felt a rough pair of hands rummaging through his trouser pockets.

"Hey!" he yelled. "No! Get off me!" He could feel his wallet being lifted from his back pocket. "Leave me alone! Don't take my wallet!"

The man on the crate turned round and looked up at Danny with the kind of expression that should have a question mark floating in the air above it.

"Hey, I'm sorry – don't get me wrong. It's simple –" Danny tried to explain. The man stood up and walked over to where Danny's torso was hanging through the wall.

"Have you got all your toys in your cupboard?" he asked. "You should take a little water with it, kid." Danny felt the same rough hands unfastening the laces to his sneakers.

"Not my sneakers!" he yelled. "They're new. They're my favourite pair! Leave me alone, whoever you are!"

As Danny felt the cold wind whipping his stockinged feet, the curly-haired man's face suddenly registered alarm.

"Keep it down, kid," he said.

"My feet!" answered Danny. "He's stolen my shoes! Help me, somebody! Help me! I'm being attacked!"

The curly-haired man threw his cigarette aside and climbed on a crate. "Go home, son," he said, "and button your lip on the way." He grabbed Danny by the arms and started pushing him backwards.

"No," said Danny, "it's not what you think! I'm –" The man gave a vigorous shove and suddenly Danny was falling. A pain shot through his right foot and his world exploded into a noisy, bad smelling maelstrom of rotten food, empty cans and broken glass.

When Danny recovered his senses, he limped wearily from the alley. His foot still hurt, his clothes were filthy and his hand was bleeding. As he passed the four men on the corner he noticed that each one of them had a brown paper bag to himself.

Danny trudged past the girl with the peanuts and began the long walk home. The wind whistled through his clothes. He thrust his hands deep in his pockets and hunched his shoulders. It was all he could do to keep from crying. Why him? Why did it always have to happen to him? Why not Leroy, Bruno, Coco? But no – Leroy was cool. He was hard. Leroy could cope.

Bruno could cope too. Sometimes he didn't look like he could tie his own shoelaces but he got by. And he had talent – what talent! That boy was going to make it big.

So was Coco. Coco had class. She shimmered. She glowed. She burned. When things got in her way she danced over them.

And Doris. He kidded around with her but she knew things he never would. She was bright. Determined. Her own woman. She could read people like a book. Not only was she good at acting -- she was funny.

And Julie – well, when you look like that and play like that, you'd be greedy to want anything else.

Thoughts tumbled round Danny's head like lottery tickets in a drum. If only he could stop being so pushy. He knew he tried too hard. Even Gene Wilder had reflective moods.

He knew the value of patience in comedy, so why did he always have to go for the wise-guy one liner? He had a lot to learn. Maybe too much. Maybe all his confidence would come to nothing. Maybe he would never climb out of the pit. Maybe he would be condemned for ever to watch, helpless, marooned, stuck fast in the mire as the other, brighter talents rose up to the stars like iron filings to a magnet.

A sudden laugh interrupted his train of thought. He was surprised to find out it came from his own throat. He looked up and saw he was nearly home. He looked down at his dirty, wet socks, his ripped trousers and his filthy jacket, and suddenly, inexplicably, a deep uncontrollable wave of laughter welled up from his stomach. Pictures of the curly haired man's face flashed through his mind. He remembered his talk with Miss Sherwood, the octopus, the window, the girl with the peanuts.

He doubled up with laughter. He shook. His sides seemed to hurt. He was an idiot. He knew it,

everybody knew it, but so what? He thought of a tramp with a brand new pair of sneakers. He thought of the image he'd had of shaking hands with Richard Pryor. He threw his head back and laughed, his heart pounding, his eyes bright, his foot aching.

He laughed at himself, at the world, at the sky. He was alive.

As Danny cleaned himself up in his room, his mother knocked on the door.

"Is everything all right?" she asked. "Was the show good? Was it funny?"

Danny felt the laughter rising again.

"Funny?" he laughed. "It was tragic!"

Albert Hague is Professor Shorofsky

When it comes to comparing Albert Hague with Professor Shorofsky, the character he plays, there is a strange sort of similarity between the two — in fact, rather a lot of similarities!

Albert Hague went to America in the 1930s from Germany. When he arrived he didn't speak English, but he did have an amazing talent for music. As he lived in America, he learned the language, and became very well known for his music, winning awards and spending the greater part of his musical career on Broadway. When it came to Professor Shorofsky, who could be more natural than Albert Hague?

Shorofsky is also a European living in America, and maybe finding it all a little too big and noisy for him. He too devotes all his energies to music, but instead of showing it to the world, he prefers to teach it to his students in *Fame*. The kids sometimes seem to look at the Professor as if he was a bit of a crank, and perhaps he is a little crusty and eccentric, but they certainly know a genius when they see one — and you can bet that, to the kids in *Fame*, Professor Shorofsky is worth his weight in gold!

Valerie Landsburg is Doris Schwarz

Valerie Landsburg grew up in the world of show business — her parents were showbiz people, and she lived in Beverley Hills, Hollywood. At school, she admits, the only class she attended seriously was drama! And, except for an interlude when she was fascinated by the study of psychology at college, she has worked in show business all her life. A successful actress, Valerie has played many roles on television and in films, as well as touring with plays and shows — and she also has a great interest in producing shows.

In *Fame*, Valerie plays bubbly Doris Schwarz, the drama student with a gift for comedy, who really wants to be a dramatic and beautiful Hollywood star, but who realises that deep down she really isn't cut out for it. Still, Doris keeps trying to achieve her aim, despite all the setbacks, and if she's anything like Valerie, she'll certainly get there!

Valerie Landsburg takes time out to listen to Albert
Hague on the piano — literally!

Morgan Stevens is David Reardon

David Reardon is a recent addition to the staff at the School for the Arts in *Fame*, teaching drama to the kids who aim for the top in show business.

Morgan Stevens, who plays David, was born in Tennessee, and is a very successful actor, having played major roles in *Quincy* and three films inspired by *The Waltons*, as well as other parts in films and television shows.

WHEN THE HEAT CAME DOWN

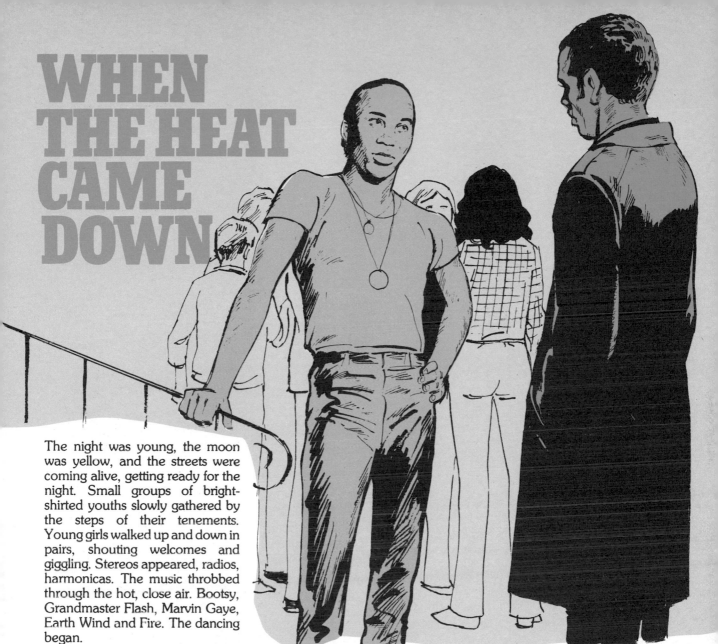

The night was young, the moon was yellow, and the streets were coming alive, getting ready for the night. Small groups of bright-shirted youths slowly gathered by the steps of their tenements. Young girls walked up and down in pairs, shouting welcomes and giggling. Stereos appeared, radios, harmonicas. The music throbbed through the hot, close air. Bootsy, Grandmaster Flash, Marvin Gaye, Earth Wind and Fire. The dancing began.

Leroy was feeling the heat. His rent was due, there'd been trouble at the poolroom, and Miss Sherwood was hot on his case, demanding five hundred words on the treatment of the Indian in modern American literature. He was trying to think of the last cowboy film he'd seen when he heard a car slow up behind him.

"Hey, boy!" said the voice. Leroy carried on walking home.

"Hey, Leroy!"

The car pulled ahead of him and stopped. Leroy's heart sank, his body tensed with anticipation.

A thin man in a long black coat climbed out of the car and stood facing him.

Leroy recognised him at once – Upstate Red, a cheap conman, a drifter, a rat – a crazed thug who'd lost his patience with time. Red came from out of town, and since he'd hit the streets he'd played it like he was already dead and living in hell.

"Hey, Leroy," said Red, offering his hand. Leroy felt the sweat on his spine go cold as Red's other hand shifted something bulky inside his coat pocket.

"I've got no business with you," he said stiffly.

"It's Willard I want."

"I'm NOT my brother's keeper."

Red leaned close and Leroy caught the rancid smell of stale whisky on his breath. "I ain't got time, boy," he said. "If I *don't* find him, they're going to find you in little parcels spread over town." He slapped Leroy on the back, climbed in his car and sped off, leaving the echo of his laughter hanging heavy in the night air.

Leroy seethed with anger and frustration. Heat clung to him like a fever. The back of his neck was damp and gritty. He beat his palm with his fist. One more weight to juggle.

He tried to weigh up his chances

as he headed for home. He could run, but not forever. He could hide. He could fight. He figured he could take Red one to one, but Red had never heard of the Marquis of Queensberry and he wasn't too proud a man to enjoy the kind of edge a sawn-off shotgun gives you.

Leroy cursed his luck as he crossed the street. He'd been on top of things. He'd been holding his life together so well. At the poolroom he was OK. The trouble from last night would blow over. At school he could make it. The writing stuff was hard but – they sure liked his dancing and they didn't pull too many numbers on him.

But Willard? There was trouble whenever he showed. Deals. Waiting. Bragging in the streets. Willard was drowning and every time Leroy helped him out was one time closer to going under with him.

Leroy stepped nimbly to one side to avoid being run over by two girl roller skaters in identical swimsuits, Kool and the Gang blaring from the stereo they held between them.

So what could he do? Well – he was a New Yorker. Native. He could survive. Red hadn't even been born in the city. Red was just a country boy with a big mouth and a gun, a hick playing fast and loose with other people's lives, a

bumpkin coming on like Pretty Boy Floyd. New York would find Red out. It always did. New York was famous all over the world. Poets came to live there, painters, writers, actors, boxers, dancers. New York had museums, nightclubs, theatres, parks, class restaurants, Wall Street, Broadway, the United Nations.

He'd be all right. It was his turf. His name was Leroy. Leroy from New York. The dancer.

He tried to think of all the famous names that had come out of New York, but a block had formed in his mind and he couldn't shift it. The only names that sprang up were Meyer Lansky and Bugsy

28

Siegel. And Al Capone. And Legs Diamond. And Johnny Torrio, Dutch Schultz, Lucky Luciano, the Gallo brothers, Joe Bananas, Lupo the Wolf and Son of Sam. And Upstate Red.

A headline on an abandoned newspaper caught Leroy's eye: STATUE OF LIBERTY FALLING DOWN.

When Leroy reached his room, he found the door had been forced. Inside, Willard was lying on his bed with a large-brimmed hat pulled down over his face. In the dim light, Leroy noticed a dark stain below the left knee of his grey trousers.

"Hi, Leroy," said Willard.

"I told you before –" Leroy began angrily.

"I need your help!" interrupted Willard. "I'm in trouble, boy!"

"If you can't do the time, don't do the crime."

"You're my brother, Leroy."

"Not any more."

Willard rose from the bed and thrust his face aggressively close to Leroy's. "This time it ain't my fault, Leroy. Upstate Red pulled a scam with the man and he's trying to lay it at my door. He's got two crazy junkies with him and if they kill me before I get a chance to talk –"

Leroy barely listened to the words, as he stood looking deep into his brother's eyes. There was no fear there, no desperate calculation. There was nothing. They were blank, the blank eyes of the doomed, the lost. Leroy knew that if he held his ground his brother would first bully him, and then, if he thought it might help, he would plead. Beg even. Leroy could not face that.

"What do you want?" he asked quietly. Willard went over to the window and peered into the street.

"They know I'm here," he said. "One of them is probably fetching Red now." He pulled up the leg of his trousers to reveal an ugly, gaping wound. "I can't outrun them like this, but if I can lose them, I can get to the man and clear myself."

"You want me to run interference?" asked Leroy, his mind flashing back to happier times, street games.

Willard took off his hat and placed it on Leroy's head. "I want you to be my decoy."

They changed clothes in silence. As Leroy made to go, Willard placed his hand on Leroy's shoulder. Leroy noticed how heavy it felt.

"Willard," he said, "I'm doing this for me – to get you out of my life for good. But –" and here a fierce light seemed to flare in his eyes, "I will never, repeat never, help you out of a jam again. In fact, if I ever *see* you again –"

"Go get 'em, tiger," said Willard, laughing and lighting a cigarette.

Leroy made his way up to the roof of his building and peered over, just in time to see Upstate Red's white-walled Chevvy come screeching to a stop in the street below. A man in a suede bomber jacket materialised from the shadows, Red got out, and they talked. Leroy picked up a stone and threw it. It bounced noisily off the bonnet of Red's car. The two men looked up the roof. Leroy waved and then grinned. The chase was on.

Leroy knew the roofs well. He had often practised there. Some nights he would just lie on his back on the roof for hours, staring at the stars in the sky. He knew he could dance Red all over them and not get caught, but he also knew there was only one other way down. If Red had a man on that exit, he was trapped.

Leroy slipped down to a lower level when he heard Red's feet on the stairs. There was a stretch of open roof ahead of him that ended with a drop to the street. Across the drop, about fifteen feet away, there

was another wall, with an old metal ladder clinging to it. Jamming Willard's hat hard down on his head and humming the Spiderman theme tune, Leroy made his run.

"Hold it there, Willard!" screamed Red, taking aim at the zig-zagging figure racing across the roof.

But the figure didn't stop. It didn't slow down. It picked up speed as it neared the drop, and when it reached the edge of the roof it soared into the air. Red was so astounded he didn't even shoot.

Leroy hit the ladder with a force that rattled every bone in his body, but he clung on tight and scrambled upwards, slipping over the lip of the roof and lying gasping with his cheek to the gravel. He could hear Red shouting down into the street.

Time was short. Leroy ran at a crouch and opened the door to the other block's stairs. He sneaked inside and ran down, taking six stairs at a time. He was three floors from the street when he came up against the first of Red's men.

Leroy didn't even break his stride. He was moving too fast to even think. No two-bit junkie was going to stop him. As the hood took aim with a Colt Python, Leroy put one hand on the stair rail and launched himself into the air.

The expression on the hood's face seemed to freeze, and for Leroy, the whole thing happened in slow motion. He was perfectly balanced, and as he dropped down to the next set of stairs he lashed out with his foot, catching the gunman a powerful blow on the upper arm. The gunman dropped his weapon, Leroy landed like a cat and kept on running.

Leroy burst into the street at full speed, ducking, dodging and weaving his way through the crowds. He raced round the corner, sprinted across some waste ground and then clawed his way up a wire fence into a basketball court. He ran the length of the court, climbed the fence at the other end, dropped down and hurried into the nearest dark alley.

Leroy flung himself against the wall and tried to catch his breath. That should have shaken them. Maybe now he could forget about Willard and get on with his life.

"What you doing, boy?" said a voice behind him. Leroy turned and saw three men in the alley. A fourth lay on the ground beside them. The largest of the men was carrying a baseball bat.

"Can't stop," said Leroy, sprinting out into the street again. Out of the corner of his eye he saw Red's car cruising round the corner further up the street.

He ran for half a block, dived down an alley and clambered over the wall at the end. He made his way through an abandoned warehouse where some old timers were playing cards and drinking, then slid into the crowds on the next street.

Leroy was walking now, trying to look inconspicuous. He thought of dumping Willard's hat but his decision became irrelevant when Red's car came into view again at the intersection ahead.

Leroy turned and ran. He heard the squeal of tyres behind him and he flew into the nearest doorway.

It was a hotel, but the desk clerk hardly had time to open his eyes before Leroy was past him and slamming through the kitchen door at the back. He caught a glimpse of a cook staring open-mouthed as he flashed through and out of the back door. As he raced out and down the back steps he heard banging and shouting behind him.

Leroy jumped across the alley and into another door. It was a store-room. He ran across it and through the open door.

"Eeeeek!" The scream came from an elderly woman trying on a flowery hat. Leroy had blundered into a hat shop.

"I'm sorry!" he said, jumping the counter and heading for the front door.

"Not so fast!" yelled a plump woman, suddenly barring his way. "Nobody steals from me!" She whipped the hat from Leroy's

head and clutched it to her chest.

"But –" Leroy didn't bother to argue. He dipped his shoulder, slipped past her and tried to open the front door as she rained heavy blows on the back of his neck.

He finally got it open, pushed his way through a gathering crowd and dived into the nearest subway. He took the first train out and settled into a seat for the long night ahead.

Coco and Bruno were deep in discussion on the steps of The School of the Arts when Leroy arrived the next morning, but they broke off when they saw him. "You look awful, man," said Bruno.

"Leroy – is anything wrong?" asked Coco.

Leroy didn't answer. He was staring at the figure leaning against the wall nearby. It was Willard.

Leroy walked straight up to him, ignoring Danny's cheery greeting and Julie's concerned gaze.

"What are you doing here?" he demanded.

Willard smiled. "We did it, Leroy," he said. "The Johnson boys did it. I saw the man and he was cool. The safest place for Red today is jail."

Leroy restrained himself from lashing out. He drove his forehead into the palm of his hand and kicked the wall.

"We did it?" he asked, his voice strained with indignation and anger. "*We* did it? *I* did it, Willard, and I nearly lost an arm and a leg doing it. I told you not to bother me. You promised to leave me alone. I've been chased all over town, I've nearly been arrested for shoplifting, I've spent all night riding the subway with a bunch of freaks and I did it because I thought I could get you off my back. I didn't want your money. I didn't want your thanks. Just WHAT are you doing here?"

"I've come for my hat," said Willard. "Leroy? . . . Leroy? That was a fifty-dollar hat, boy . . . Leroy?"

He threw his cigarette into the gutter and turned away from Leroy's retreating back.

BUDDIES...

They may be on opposite sides of the coin on screen . . .

. . . but behind the scenes . . .

. . . Leroy (Gene Anthony Ray) and

Professor Shorofsky (Albert Hague) are very good friends!

Gene Anthony Ray is Leroy

When it came to making a television series from the film of *Fame*, Gene Anthony Ray was a must for the character of Leroy, having played the part so successfully on the big screen. His success has been remarkable, not least because he had had no formal dance training prior to his film role, despite his amazing agility and sense of rhythm.

Leroy is essentially a loner, the 'bad guy' of the show, always falling foul of his teachers and

yet always coming out on top, his sulky manner being his trademark. Gene himself is also a loner, but his attitude is rather that of a shy person than that of a rebel. He and Leroy are by no means one and the same person, although Gene's portrayal of the character is based to a great extent on his own experiences. And there is no doubt at all in the minds of *Fame* fans that Gene Anthony Ray is a 'natural' — he *is* Leroy Johnson!

Carlo Imperato is Danny Amatullo

A native New Yorker, Carlo Imperato was born in the Bronx, and unlike many of the stars of *Fame*, his parents were not involved in the theatre. Carlo went to an ordinary school until he auditioned for and won a part on a show called *The Runaways* which ran for a year on Broadway. Carlo continued his education after this first success at the Professional Children's School, and went on to many other roles before winning the part of Danny Amatullo in *Fame*.

Danny Amatullo is the show's comedian,

never short of a joke to crack, but discovering along the way that life is a lot more serious than he would like to believe. Luckily for Danny, he always bounces back after his numerous disappointments, refusing to be beaten, and it is this which makes him so popular.

Carlo's major passion is acting, of course, but when he has a moment to spare, he loves playing American football, basketball and soccer.

NUTS

is all about but – I don't know what it's like to be old, defeated, without hope."

"You don't know what it's like to date Al Pacino either," said Danny.

Reardon ignored him.

"Observation, Doris," he explained, and suddenly his whole body slumped. "Her legs hurt. Her hips hurt. She's carried too many shopping bags in her time. Her expression is pinched –"

"Where from?"

"Her expression is pinched, mean, hurt. But –" And here, with unusual accuracy, Reardon mimed an elderly lady climbing stairs with an armful of shopping and backache. "She still has her pride. The world may have left her out of its plans, but she's still in there pitching." He stood up straight and addressed himself to the whole class. "You can learn just so much from books, but your biggest and best reference library is right outside the window. They're all out there, the heroes, the villains, the saints and the crazy men, the desperate, the caring, the unfeeling, the lost, the beaten, the brave – all you've got to do is look."

"And make sure they don't catch you doing it," muttered Danny.

It was cold when Doris got to Central Park that weekend, but she didn't let it put her off. She was there to work, to observe, to improve her craft, to draw from the deep well of human experience some nugget of truth – and it was a pretty good chance to show off her new woolly hat. She'd already been whistled at twice and the young man with the deely boppers had been extremely pleasant right up to the moment he'd tried to steal her watch.

Her first stop was the Bethseda Fountain. A gang of greasers sat drinking nearby, acting surly. A shaven-headed woman in an immaculate three piece suit danced barefoot in front of them. Lovers kissed. Families shared picnics. Children squabbled and played. Two men on skateboards, backed by an all-girl acoustic band, sang about the perils of eating meat. An

Reardon clapped his hands and the rehearsal stopped. "Doris," he said patiently, placing his arm gently round her shoulders, " the part you're supposed to be playing is a housewife about to flip her lid, right?"

"Right," agreed Doris.

"She's had it up to here." Reardon made a stiff salute to his eyes. "She's been scratching and scraping for nearly forty years to keep body and soul together. Her husband can't hold down a job. She can hardly bear to be in the same room as him."

"You know the feeling," said Doris, flashing Danny a smile.

"Her kids never write to her, the neighbours never speak, they've stopped her credit at the grocery store, all she ever sees on TV is bad news and violence. This woman has had enough, right?"

"Right," agreed Doris again. Reardon allowed himself a theatrical roll of the eyes.

"Then why are you playing her like she was on a first date with Al Pacino?"

"You got me there. I suppose, well – I know that this is what acting

old man with dark glasses handed Doris a badge that had on it a mushroom cloud and the words HECK NO — WE WON'T GLOW. "Now let me take a picture," he said, fastening the badge to the lapel of Doris's coat. "You look awful pretty in that hat."

He raised his camera and took a shot of Doris standing by the fountain.

"You an actress?" he asked. "You've got something about you, you know?"

"You really think so?"

"Sure," he said, peeling off the covering to the instant picture. "That'll be five bucks."

"What?"

"Five bucks — c'mon, it's a good picture. Five bucks."

Doris started walking away.

The man grabbed her arm. "What do you think I am? A charity? Five bucks, lady!"

"I haven't got five bucks."

"I should have known it," snarled the man, ripping the photograph into small bits and stamping on them. "You're too fat to have class! You hear that, pear-drop? Go on! Get out of here!"

Doris was only too pleased to. She made her way down to Conservatory Lake and watched the courting couples in their rowing boats trying to avoid the presence of a giant canoe crammed with young men and women with green Mohican haircuts and identical green jackets, who were trying to capsize every boat that came near them.

"You wanna buy a watch?"

"Huh?"

"You wanna buy a watch, girl?"

The speaker was a sallow skin-ned girl of around Doris's age.

"No."

"C'mon — they're good watches." She pulled up her sleeve. There were seven different watches strapped to her arm.

"What's the time?" asked Doris.

"Hey! C'mon — these are good watches!"

"What's the time?"

The girl peered at the watch with the largest face and then pulled her sleeve down.

"It's a quarter to," she said.

"A quarter to what?" asked Doris.

"I said it was a quarter to," she said indignantly, turning to leave. It was twelve twenty.

Doris made for the zoo, passing a group of long-haired bearded men playing what seemed to be tennis, but with no racket and no ball. She stopped briefly to listen to a man in a loin cloth denouncing New York's archaic betting laws, and she felt a warm glow when the driver of a horse-drawn cab raised his hat to her and bowed as he passed.

At the zoo, Doris pulled faces at the monkeys and laughed out loud when she saw a little boy pulling his tongue out at a snake. A man with an easel sat before an empty cage, telling anyone who would listen that he was the son of a sabre-toothed tiger. At the café, she

bought herself a glass of milk.

For nearly an hour, Doris watched the visitors to the zoo. At the next table, two impossibly thin model girls drank cokes and ate double cheeseburgers with all the trimmings. From the snatches of conversation that came her way, it seemed to Doris that the main trouble with their lives was the differing colour of the upholstery inside their boyfriends' otherwise identical limousines.

Doris turned her attention to the parade of families, friends, loners and freaks who ignored the DO NOT FEED THE ANIMALS signs, until her observations were interrupted by an extremely young boy with a green baize cloth who came and sat at her table, talking fast in a language Doris could not place.

"Yes?" said the boy, spreading the green cloth out before Doris. On it were marked drawings of

several cards bearing symbols — hearts, diamonds, club, spades, a pelican and a skull and crossbones. The boy began a long monologue that Doris found incomprehensible.

"Yes?" said the boy again, producing some dice from his pocket.

"No," said Doris.

The boy threw the dice and stared at them like a witch doctor studying bones. Doris finished her milk.

"A dollar – yes?" said the boy, pointing first to the dice and then to the skull and crossbones.

"No," said Doris, getting up to go.

"A dollar!" said the boy. "A measly dollar!" He held out one hand and began folding up the cloth with the other.

"Get lost, shrimp," said Doris, picking up her bag and making to leave. "I don't have a dollar."

The boy wasn't listening. He was approaching a silver-haired couple in matching crimplene suits. Doris walked to a bench and pulled out her sandwiches while three middle-aged men did wheelies on their bicycles in front of her.

As Doris ate her cucumber sandwiches she began to wonder if she had made the right decision joining the School of the Arts. Sure, the performing arts were an important mirror on mankind's aspirations and failings, an illumination of people's hopes and fears, but . . . Her attention was drawn by a quick scurrying movement on the ground to her right.

It was a small grey squirrel. One of its eyes was covered by a milky film and most of the hair on its haunches was missing. It stared at Doris with its one good eye, and when Doris held out a piece of lettuce it scampered forward.

"Here you are," said Doris, holding out the lettuce close to the squirrel's mouth.

The squirrel ignored it and sank its teeth deep into Doris's hand.

"Hey! Let go!" shouted Doris, pulling her hand away. The squirrel let go and ran off. Doris looked at the blood oozing from the wound between her thumb and her forefinger.

"Ungrateful little rat!" she hissed, as the squirrel climbed a tree. Doris wrapped her hand in her handkerchief and went back to the zoo to buy something to put on it. The first person she saw was a young zoo attendant with blonde hair and black eyes.

"You did what?" he asked, when Doris had explained what had happened.

"I was feeding this squirrel and –"

"Has nobody told you not to feed squirrels without gloves?" the

man asked angrily.

"My name's Doris," said Doris.

"Kirk," said the man. "Kirk Walters. You got any money?"

"No."

"Come with me then."

Kirk took Doris down to a hospital on 42nd street. On the way, he gave her the low-down on squirrel bites. "There's rabies of course, and lockjaw . . . not to mention Bu."

"Bu?"

"Bubonic plague," Kirk explained, opening his car door and pointing the way to the hospital waiting room. "It's not impossible. And typhoid, tetanus, cholera — have you had your injections?"

Doris wasn't sure. The only thing she wanted to do was go home. Kirk sat her on a bench in the waiting room and went to find a doctor. On one side of her was a bearded man in tennis shorts, and on the other was an enormous woman with a star tattooed on her forehead and a Mickey Mouse hat on her head. "Don't ever touch my bag," she said softly.

"I won't," said Doris nervously. The woman had no bag.

Kirk came back with a nurse who was carrying a bowl full of clear liquid. "Soak your finger in this," said the nurse.

Doris placed her finger in the bowl and two policemen came over with a noisy, thin, leather-jacketed girl handcuffed between them.

"The nurse says you were bitten by a squirrel," said one.

"That's right," answered Doris.

"Could you identify the squirrel if you saw it again?"

Doris stifled a scream, picked up her bag and ran home.

The following Monday, having been reassured by her mother's doctor that she was not about to drop dead, Doris was back in the drama class reading a part with Julie and Coco.

"It's no good, Mr Reardon," she said. "This part is too thin. The person doesn't exist. She's anaemic. She's just there to help the plot along."

"I agree the part is not one of Miller's best," said Reardon, "but it's up to you to flesh it out. That's acting."

"You think a change of costume would make the part more meaty?" asked Doris.

"Yeah," said Danny. "Designer jeans — by Moby Dick."

Reardon sighed. "It's not costume that makes up a character," he said. "It's what's inside. Dress can be an extension of somebody's character, but it can also be a disguise. The fact that dress is a readily-accepted status indicator means that it is open to subversion and manipulation."

"You're saying that a man dressed like a tramp could just as easily be a bank president?"

"I'm saying we must try and break away from the general assumptions about how people dress."

"I always put my socks on last," said Danny.

Doris was looking puzzled. "Mr Reardon," she began. "What do you make of a grown man who stands on a soap box in the freezing cold wearing only a loin cloth?"

"Huh?"

"Or a group of boys and girls with matching Mohican haircuts — green? Hippies that play tennis with no rackets or balls? Model girls who do nothing but eat and bicker? Women with Mickey Mouse hats and stars tattooed on their foreheads? Bald barefoot women in three piece suits?"

"It's probably an affirmation of their individual—" Reardon paused. "Did you say a loin cloth? In this weather?"

Doris nodded.

"Green hair? Stars?"

"Yep."

"Nuts."

"That's what I thought," Doris affirmed. "Nuts."

Erica Gimpel is Coco Hernandez

Perhaps the most bubbly and ambitious character in *Fame* is Coco Hernandez, and Erica Gimpel captures her personality right down to the ground. Originally a student at the School of the Arts in New York, Erica loves dancing, acting and music, although she confesses to a love of rollerskating — the only thing which might tempt her away from her classes, and which undoubtedly keeps her so fit!

Having been an actress since her childhood, Erica Gimpel intends one day to try camping, perhaps in Australia or Portugal, countries she visited with her mother when she was a child. But whether the producers of *Fame* will allow this very talented actress to disappear into the wilds with a tent remains to be seen!

LEE'S SONG

It was lunchtime in The School of the Arts and the band were in full flight, with Leroy and Coco stalking the floor trading lines, the insistent, rhythmic movements of their bodies speaking loud – we're young and proud.

Behind them the lead guitar fought a grim duel with the sax, circling, soaring, swooping, sparking as they touched, retreating and coming back for more.

The drums rolled and thundered, the throbbing bass pumped out wall-shaking loops, and through this torrent of sound, like a salmon fighting its way upstream, Bruno's piano leapt in with a series of bright, instinctive, magically rippling runs.

The reason Bruno's playing was largely instinctive was that he wasn't concentrating on either the singers or the song. The only thing he could think of was the bass

player's soft, shiny, silken hair. It was jet black, and as she stood close beside him he imagined he could smell her shampoo, an elusive fragrance that seemed to stir things inside him.

And the way it fell across her face... her quick, economical movements... her blue eyes, her cheekbones, her lips... she seemed to Bruno like some nervous woodland animal, but she played the bass with more bite than an angry cobra. It was a miracle anyone heard the bell.

"Shoot," said Coco, the spell broken. She brushed the hair from her face and bent down to pick up her books. Bruno hardly noticed. The bass player was looking straight into his eyes, and, unless those very same eyes deceived him, she liked what she saw.

"Say, you're not bad," she said. Bruno cursed himself for blush-

ing. "You play a pretty solid bass," he replied.

"You want to hear me on the cello."

"You're kidding. What class are you in?"

"None. I just came down to see the Professor."

"Shorofsky?"

"Sure. We're old friends. What's your name?"

"Bruno. Bruno Martelli."

"Pleased to meet you, Bruno. My name's Lee. Lee Rand."

One quick smile later and she was gone.

But for Bruno the smile remained. It hovered in front of his eyes as he picked up his books and went to class. He shook his head and blinked but it would not go away. The stirrings of a brand new song began. A song for Lee. Could it be that, at long last, Angelo Martelli's favourite son was finally going to fall?

A week passed with no sign of Lee. In the music class before lunch, Professor Shorofsky was just getting into his stride. "When any musical culture is plundered for gain – when it is popularised, trivialised, commercialised; when a deep-rooted culture is turned into a passing fad by people who do not understand it, do not try to understand it, just squeeze it when the time is opportune . . ." He leaned back and closed his eyes. "When such a school of music – or thought – has been thus abused, the tendency of those left behind is to turn away from those who have abused them, to dig deeper into their own past, to follow their own roots down until they hit rock, and then to polish that rock and –" He opened his eyes and, as usual, the first person he noticed was Bruno. It was obvious Bruno wasn't listening. "Bruno?" he said softly.

Bruno didn't reply. He was still trying to shake the smile from his mind.

"Martelli! See me after class!" Bruno blinked and then nodded.

When the class was over and he and Bruno were alone, Professor Shorofsky tried to choose his words carefully. For once he failed. "Why do I have the feeling I've been here before?" he asked.

"Professor?"

Shorofsky sighed. There was a knock on the door. "Come in."

Suddenly Lee was there and Bruno's heart felt like it was playing host to a tiny juggler.

"That will be all, Bruno," said Shorofsky.

"Unh?"

"Martelli – go."

Bruno picked up his books and headed for the door. As he passed Lee she gave him a reprise of her stunning smile.

"See you for lunch?" she asked.

"Sure," said Bruno. "I'll be in the lunchroom."

Bruno went to the lunchroom and took a seat next to Danny, Doris and Julie.

"Do you think Mr Reardon's right in his interpretation of Blanche's character?" asked Doris.

"I think he's reading too much into it," said Julie. "*Streetcar* is a pretty straightforward piece, in that any Tennessee Williams work can be called straightforward."

"I look at it this way," said Danny, grabbing his left shoulder blade with his right hand and staring at the ceiling.

Once again, Bruno wasn't listening. In his mind, all he could see was Lee's face, all he could hear was the melody that had been haunting him since they had met. And into that melody, as if from nowhere, a jumble of words fell and were immediately caught, and held firm.

I'VE SEEN THE HARBOUR LIGHTS
THE BIRDS IN THE TREES
LOVE ON A SUMMER'S NIGHT
LEAVES IN THE BREEZE
AND OUT OF ALL THE SIGHTS
IT'S BEEN MY PLEASURE TO SEE
NOTHING LOOKS QUITE SO RIGHT
AS THAT SMILE OF LEE'S
NOTHING IS QUITE AS BRIGHT
AS THAT SMILE OF LEE'S
THAT BEAUTIFUL SMILE OF LEE'S

Bruno caught a faint trace of a familiar smell, and suddenly Lee was sitting beside him, offering him an apple from a brown paper bag. Bruno took it.

"The Professor tells me you're his main man," she said.

"He knows that I love music."

"So do I."

They talked. Hopes, dreams.

Bruno felt himself being drawn further and further into the mystery of Lee's smile. Doris's sharp comments went unnoticed. Julie's attempts to join the conversation were ignored. Even Danny couldn't break into the bubble that seemed to surround them, a fact that did nothing to improve his humour.

"That Bruno," he said to Doris in a loud stage whisper. "With his first cigar he made himself sick. Now, with his first girl, he makes everyone else sick."

Neither Bruno nor Lee appeared to have heard. When the time came for Lee to leave and Bruno to return to his lessons, a firm date had been fixed for that evening.

Bruno spent the afternoon in a daze. The song he had written about Lee played itself over and over in his mind like a loop tape, and every time it played he made some minor adjustments – strings here, a longer break there, maybe a lone sax crying in the distance.

When he reached home he thought it was just about as good as it was going to get.

"Ah, Bruno," said his father, welcoming him with a large mug of coffee, "you write some beautiful music today?"

"Is it okay to bring someone home tonight, Pop?" asked Bruno.

"A girl?" said Angelo hopefully. "Coco maybe? Or Julie? A beautiful girl that Julie. Not Italian of course, but beautiful all the same. Fine cheekbones."

"It's not Julie."

"It's Doris?" Angelo opened his palms and leant his head to one side. "A nice girl. No Botticelli perhaps, but a good girl. A very nice girl."

The doorbell spared Bruno from any more of his father's match-making. It was Lee.

"Lee, this is my father."

"Pleased to meet you, Mr Martelli."

"Angelo, please. To a beautiful

girl like you my name is Angelo." He took her hand, kissed it and made a small bow. "You want to eat?"

Angelo sat them at the kitchen table and brought out coleslaw, several slices of pizza, a piece of cheese and some bread.

"You want soup?" he asked.

Bruno and Lee laughed.

"We're OK, Papa," said Bruno, "this is fine."

"It's fine," agreed Lee, "this is fine."

Angelo put his hand on Lee's shoulder. "Well, if you want some more," he said, "you make sure he gives it to you, right?"

He slapped her cheek affectionately. "Me? I must go. You think cabs run themselves?"

"Goodbye, Angelo," said Lee. "Ciao."

Bruno and Lee finished their food and went down into the basement. Bruno offered Lee a chair. "Here," he said, "sit down.

There's something I want you to hear."

Lee sat down and Bruno played her the tune he had written for her. Lee closed her eyes and smiled as the melody swelled through the room.

"Hey, that was great, big boy," she said, clapping her hands when Bruno finally stopped. "Paul McCartney will be shaking in his boots."

"You want to bid for the concession on Bruno wigs?"

"And dolls, and boots. Have you got a lyric for it?"

"I've got a lyric," said Bruno quietly. "It's for you. In the words

of the immortal Elton John/Bernie Taupin smash – *This is Your Song.*"

And then Bruno played it again, this time adding the lyrics that had come so naturally, starting off slowly, sadly even, and then building up to a heartfelt climax of such emotional intensity that he felt embarrassed in the silence that followed.

"Sentimental slush, huh?" he asked, staring at the back of his hands.

Lee got up and held them with her own. "It was beautiful, Bruno," she said. "The Professor was right about you."

"How come you know the Professor anyway?" asked Bruno.

"I used to study with him. He was always kind, always good."

"Why did you leave the school?"

Lee let Bruno's hands go. Her voice became flatter, harder. "It's an old story, and not a very interesting one. There was trouble at home. My dad split, my mother couldn't handle the pressure. We needed money. Professor Shorofsky did all he could to help us, but it wasn't enough."

"But you've got talent. Great talent. I've heard you play."

"It's not enough, Bruno," said Lee. "Music can transcend all

"I did – at one time. But things change, people change. The reason I was back at the school was that the Professor had offered me a place back on the course. I was going to refuse it – until I met you."

"And now?"

"You can't go back, Bruno. It's wrong to even try. When I saw how you and Coco and Julie were so involved, so dedicated, for a moment I thought –"

"You thought what?" said Bruno, a hint of anger in his voice. "You could still do it. I know you could."

"My time's gone, Bruno – with that kind of music anyway. You've got to give it all you've got, and I don't have it to give."

"And me?"

Lee got up and reached for her coat. "You're going to make it, Bruno," she said. "You're going to go all the way. But it's going to be a long ride, and I don't want to take it."

"But –"

"Hey, Bruno," said Lee, slipping into her coat and flashing her old, dazzling grin. "Don't give me a hard time, okay?" She leant for-

barriers of language, race, age – and the Professor is right to revere it. But up there," she gestured to the ceiling with her thumb, "the name of the game is hustle. There's people who buy and people who are bought. One of my mother's friends fixed me up with a job at Brownlow and MacAlpine's."

"The advertising people?"

"That's right." Lee smiled with her mouth but her eyes remained cold. "And now my mother's on the mend, my brothers are doing well at school and at the end of every month I'm holding the folding."

"But you miss the school?"

ward and kissed him gently on the cheek. "Maybe we'll meet one day in Vegas."

"But the song – I wrote it for you."

"It was beautiful."

"It's yours."

Lee laughed. "What would I want with sentimental slush?"

Bruno smiled ruefully. "I know," he said, "I guess I was getting a little carried away. I just thought you'd like it, that maybe you could do something with it."

Lee kissed him again and turned to go. "Maybe one day I will."

It took Bruno nearly two months to get over Lee. In that time he threw himself into his music with such determination that even Professor Shorofsky had expressed a cautious satisfaction. Now, as he headed for the school in the back of his father's cab, he was back in the swing, fighting fit and raring to go.

"Hey," said Angelo, fiddling with the dial on his radio, "what happened to that girl Lee? A very smart cookie, that Lee, with beautiful legs."

"She's around," said Bruno,

affecting nonchalance. "We were just –" Bruno stopped as a familiar refrain came crackling over the airwaves.

I'VE SEEN THE HARBOUR LIGHTS
THE BIRDS IN THE TREES
LOVE ON A SUMMER'S NIGHT
LEAVES IN THE BREEZE . . .

"Hey, this is good!" said Angelo, turning the radio up. "Not as good as your stuff, but good, all the same."

AND OUT OF ALL THE SIGHTS
IT'S BEEN MY PLEASURE TO SEE . . .

"Hey, this sounds familiar, Bruno. You sure it's not one of yours?"

NOTHING LOOKS QUITE SO RIGHT
AS PINKERTON'S BEANS
NOTHING TASTES QUITE SO RIGHT
AS PINKERTON'S BEANS
A PLATE FULL OF PINKERTON'S BEANS.

Bruno shook his head and laughed to himself. "No, Pop," he said, "it's not one of mine."

IDENTITY CRISIS

W inter came early. There was sunshine one day, and it seemed – next day, icy winds and snow. Dry, shrivelled leaves blew about on the sidewalks, sometimes whipped up as high as people's heads. Doris's teeth chattered as she walked to The School of the Arts, and she pulled her woollen hat down further over her eyes, and her scarf higher up over her chin.

"Hey! Doris!" yelled Leroy as he ran up to her. "You late again?"

"What is it to you?" Doris said crossly. She stumbled over her feet. "Now look what you've made me do."

"Man, you can't blame me for that," Leroy said, grinning. "Maybe if you looked where you're going you wouldn't do it. Anyone ever tell you about that thing on your head looking really stupid?"

"Anyone ever tell you about your big mouth being always open?" retorted Doris, pulling off the hat and stuffing it into her pocket.

"Ma'am," said Leroy, bowing low with mock humility. "I beg your pardon, ma'am. Can you ever forgive me, ma'am?"

"Get lost, Johnson," said Doris irritably. Leroy shrugged his shoulders and strode on ahead.

"What's bitten Doris?" he asked Julie Miller just before their English class later that day.

Julie looked across to where Doris sat, her head in her hands, her eyes staring off into the distance. "I thought she'd have got over that by now," she said, shaking her head.

"Got over what?" demanded Leroy. "She hasn't fallen for some guy, has she?"

"Of course not," Julie said, smiling. "Doris doesn't get herself into situations like that. Besides, who could she fall for round here? No, she's still sore about being left out of *Macbeth*."

"Man, that was weeks ago!" Leroy said in surprise. "How come it's still bothering Doris? Everyone has to have their turn, don't they?"

Julie nodded. "Yeah, but Doris really takes it as some sort of personal insult. You know how she wants to be the greatest actress in America, and how she always wants to play the leading part."

"Yeah," agreed Leroy, "but Doris is a comedy actress. She makes people laugh. Her playing Lady Macbeth would be like Professor Shorofsky playing John Travolta."

Julie opened her book as Miss Sherwood entered the room.

"You try telling her that! She just won't accept it – I've tried to explain it to her, and she just bit my head off!"

"Good morning, class," said Miss Sherwood, perching herself on the edge of her desk. "You'll be pleased to know that we're doing a production of Shakespeare's *A Midsummer Night's Dream* as part of the Christmas celebrations in school. *And* we're going to do it really well, Leroy." She pointed to a stack of books beside her. "So I want everyone to take one copy of the play home with them, and read through it. This will be your assignment for the week, OK?"

Julie and Leroy exchanged glances, then looked across at Doris. She was looking at Miss Sherwood's pile of books, and the

listless look had left her face.

Julie leaned across to Leroy once again. "Are you thinking what I'm thinking?" she whispered.

Leroy nodded. "I certainly am," he muttered in reply, grinning.

"Doris wants to *direct* it?" Danny Amatullo asked incredulously. "Why? Who's going to take any notice of Doris as a director? They won't be able to take her seriously."

Coco nodded. "And when there's a part here that could have been written just for her, too."

"Which part's that?" asked Leroy over her shoulder.

"Haven't you read the play?" Danny asked.

Leroy shrugged. "Some. I'm not an actor. All those words get me confused. It's not even in English. All those 'doths' and 'forsooths'."

Coco sighed. "Leroy, you're a real philistine. Anyhow, you'd better start reading the play. All of it."

"Why?" demanded Leroy.

"Miss Sherwood has put your name down for the part of Oberon, that's why."

Leroy groaned, as Julie came up to them.

"I'm down as Helena!" she said in dismay. "What am I going to do? I can't act. I wanted to do the music with Bruno."

"Well, I'm supposed to be Hermia," said Coco. "She's supposed to be small, and that's something I ain't. That's the part for Doris, Leroy. I'd much rather direct the play."

"And you'd be good, too," said Danny gloomily. "What are we going to do?"

They stood in dumb silence for a moment. Then Julie clapped her hands.

"Got it!" she cried. "I know what we can do. Everyone will have to do their best, or it won't work. Now, listen . . ."

Snow was falling over New York, and although it was the middle of the day, the sky was quite dark and overcast.

In Central Park, a group of children were running about in the snow, leaving their footprints in the smooth whiteness. The sounds of

the city were strangely muffled, as if the snow was a thick blanket over everything, but as she sat on a wet bench Doris was oblivious to all of it anyway. She was leaning forward over her copy of *A Midsummer Night's Dream*, a notebook lying open on her lap. In it she was jotting down notes as she went through the play – this person to move here, that one to move there, and to say the lines in such a way. She could see it all so clearly in her mind's eye – she was sure it would be perfect. If only everyone – including the difficult Leroy – would do things just as she wanted, it would be the best performance the School had ever given. She was sure of it. She just wished this directing were easier.

"I just don't believe it!" said Elizabeth Sherwood to Lydia Grant over her cup of coffee. "Leroy

Johnson actually reading the play, *and* making sense of it! It's incredible. I keep thinking that something *has* to go wrong. Things *can't* be that smooth."

"Is that in a rehearsal?" queried Lydia.

Elizabeth shook her head. "No, in class. The first rehearsal's this afternoon, and I must say I'm not looking forward to it. But if – and this is a very big if – Leroy and the others can keep it up, it might be OK. Doris is directing it."

"*Doris?*" repeated Lydia in disbelief. "So who's playing Hermia?"

Elizabeth sighed heavily. "Coco Hernandez."

Lydia whistled. "And she cut Doris out of being Hermia? Elizabeth, really . . ."

"No, no," said Elizabeth. "Doris insisted on being director, despite all I could say to her. I think she's

still sore about being cut out of *Macbeth*, and has lost her confidence."

"But surely she realises that she's not the Lady Macbeth type?" asked Lydia. "She's one of the best comedy actresses we've got at this school. But tragedy just isn't her line. Should we say something to her about it?"

Elizabeth shook her head. "I think it might be better to let the kids talk to her or something. She'll never take kindly to us giving her a lecture about it. I think she knows it really, but just doesn't want to admit to it. She may have some dreams about becoming another Sarah Bernhardt, and she's got to realise that she isn't cut out for it."

"Sounds like this is the snag you've been looking for, Elizabeth dear," said Lydia, getting up, and smiling at her colleague. "What are you going to do about it?"

"I'm not going to do anything at all," Elizabeth said firmly. "I'm going to let events take their course, and hope that Doris comes to her senses in time for Christmas."

"Good luck!" said Lydia, waving goodbye to her cheerfully. "You'll need it."

The cast of *A Midsummer Night's Dream* sat around, chattering and talking. Leroy was reading through his lines once again, his lips moving as he went over the words. Coco and Julie stood talking in hushed voices, while Danny Amatullo listened to their conversation. Bruno tried out a couple of bars of his music on the piano and Miss Sherwood sat at the back of the room, wondering if this show was ever going to get off the ground.

"Sorry I'm late!" said Doris breathlessly as she burst through the door. "I got held up by some people. I won't be a minute – is everyone else ready to start?"

The play got underway, Doris consulting her notebook and constantly getting up to pull people by the arm into the positions she had worked out for them. As she did this at times when people were in the middle of saying their lines, her actions produced a lot of giggling and laughter, and Miss Sherwood sighed from her seat at the back of the room.

"No, no, no," Doris was saying. "Coco, don't say it like that. Put the emphasis on the third word, not the second."

Coco and Julie Miller exchanged glances, and then Coco repeated the lines almost exactly as she had just said them. Doris jumped off her chair.

"You still haven't got it right! Say it again – no, not just that line, the

whole thing. You can see how Hermia would have said that line from what goes before it. Do it again."

Obediently Coco flipped back the pages of her script, and began the speech again. This time it was even worse. Leroy glanced at Doris – she was shaking her head impatiently as she followed the lines with her finger. Leroy smiled. At the back of the room, Miss Sherwood sat up suddenly, watching him. What was Leroy Johnson playing at? Her gaze passed to other members of the cast – Julie and Bruno were pretending to study their scripts, while Danny, behind Doris's back, was grinning at Leroy. Miss Sherwood clasped her hands together. She wasn't sure what was going on, but was – oddly – reluctant to interfere. At that moment, Lydia Grant crept in to the room on tiptoe, and made her way over to kneel beside her friend.

"How's it going?" she whispered.

Elizabeth shook her head, putting one finger against her lips, her eyes fixed on the stage. Lydia followed her gaze.

"Are you stupid or something?" Doris was demanding crossly.

"the teachers won't do nothing neither if you don't play that part. That's how it is. All out strike!"

Doris stared round at her friends. "You rats!" she said at last. "You had me set up, didn't you? You knew that once I played that part you'd never be able to get me off it."

Her friends closed around her once more, Coco excitedly saying that she had wanted to direct the play all along. Miss Sherwood turned to Lydia Grant.

"Snag over?" she asked. Lydia shook her head.

"You just wait," she said, smiling, "until Leroy realises that Danny Amatullo as Puck has far more dancing to do than Leroy as Oberon. Then you *will* have a strike on your hands!"

Elizabeth stared at her in horror. "Oh, no! I never thought of that!"

"I wish you luck!" smiled Lydia, and pirouetted out of the room.

"That was awful! You sounded like a bad politician. Everyone else is fine. What's wrong with *you*, Coco?"

"Well, I don't know what you want," Coco flashed back at her. "You haven't said how it is you want me to say the thing! It's your directing, Doris. I just don't understand it."

There was a pause. Miss Sherwood gripped her pen tightly.

"Man," drawled Leroy, "this is really boring, you know? Why can't we just go home? All this is just a waste of time when Coco can't do it right . . ."

"Oh, come on," said Doris angrily. "Coco, get down off that stage. I'll have to show you what I want you to say. Why do I have to do everything myself?"

She clambered up on to the stage, clutching her script.

"Now," said Doris, "this is what I want, Coco. Listen and pay attention."

She began to read the lines, her voice rising and falling as each new emotion was felt by the character of Hermia. It was as if quite suddenly, Doris Schwarz had stopped being Doris Schwarz, and had

actually become Hermia. Dressed as she was in her jeans and jumper, with her sneakers on her feet, she might have been wearing full period costume and make-up. One could almost see the forest around her, smell the grass and the trees . . .

"Now," Doris said, reaching the end of the speech. "Now do you see?"

But she got no further. Her voice was drowned by a burst of clapping and cheering from the rest of the kids and the two teachers. They surrounded her, patting her on the back, congratulating her. Doris began to laugh.

"Hey, what is this? All I did was to show Coco what I wanted. Have you got it now, Coco?"

"I'll never get it like you got it," Coco said. "How can you expect me to play that part after you just did all that? You *are* Hermia, Doris."

"Yeah," agreed Leroy, "that's your part, Doris. *You* don't play it, *we* don't do nothing."

"We don't do *anything*," corrected Miss Sherwood, coming forward.

"See, Doris," continued Leroy,

Debbie Allen is Lydia Grant

Like the character she plays, Debbie Allen is a remarkable lady! Not only does she astound *Fame* fans with her amazing dancing ability, but she choreographs all the dance routines for the other stars, and sings her own powerful vocals to the original music we hear in *Fame*. She acted in, choreographed and produced the stage show that toured Britain in late 1982.

While studying for her BA degree, Debbie filled her spare time with ballet classes, and one of her first roles was on Broadway — the goal of every American performer. From such great beginnings, Debbie went on to major roles in

such successful shows as *Roots: The Next Generations* and *Guys and Dolls*, as well as a whole host of others.

Lydia Grant, the character Debbie plays in *Fame*, is a little like her in that she insists on the best every time, and never settles for anything else. Lydia drives her students on until they reach perfection — and only then is she satisfied. And although they might resent such a powerful driving force, all Lydia's students will thank her from the bottom of their hearts when, at last, they reach the fame they all seek!

DUELLING DANCERS

Despite the warmth of the autumn sun outside, Lydia shivered as she lined up her students for their first work-out of the day. Her exceptional physical condition made it difficult for her to identify with the colds, snuffles, aches and pains that seemed to affect so many New Yorkers once the boiling summer had gone.

"OK, you guys," she said briskly, "let's go."

But even as she led her class through their warming-up exercises, Lydia knew she was sickening for something. She was so rarely ill that she didn't know what it might be, but she knew she wasn't right. Of course she would fight it, ignore it, work twice as hard to try and shake it off, but it looked like it was going to be one of those mornings she'd be glad just to get through.

Lydia walked along the line of students now exercising at the barre. "Mm – that's good, Julie . . . a little higher, Leroy – a little more reach . . ."

Lydia cajoled, encouraged, advised, until the exercise was over. She then drew the students round her in a circle, knelt on the floor and went through a series of extremely taxing movements with her upper body, stretching, pulling, slashing, dabbing, flicking, pressing and floating.

"You see," she said, getting to her feet, "these movements in a dance make a great contrast with the flying movements."

"You mean like this?" said Coco, breaking into a sudden fluid sequence of flashing, twisting jumps.

"Not quite like that," said Lydia, rather coldly. Perhaps the hardest thing she had to teach Coco was that she still had a lot to learn.

"Like how, then?" asked Coco, hands on her hips.

Lydia began a well-practised dance routine that was designed to show just how much more spectacular movements in leaps, skips and jumps can be made to look when set against the same movements performed sitting or lying on the floor. It was a difficult routine, but one she knew well, and it came as a shock to her when at the end of a particularly acrobatic leap and kick, her leg buckled on landing and she crashed to the floor in a heap.

The first person to offer Lydia a helping hand was Coco. Lydia refused it, climbed to her feet and shook herself down.

"One more time," she said quietly.

Coco took up a position slightly behind her. "Mind if I tag along for the ride?"

Lydia did mind. She wasn't in the mood to have Coco showing off at her expense. She would rather have called time on the lesson and taken ten with a glass of warm milk. But the amused, insolent glint in Coco's eye told her

that if she backed off on this one her grip on Coco's attention – and therefore her one real hope of disciplining Coco's wonderful talent – might be weakened forever.

Lydia led off, slowly at first, using her hands like letters of the alphabet, arranging her movements into words, statements, poems.

Behind her Coco matched her every move. She was feeling good. She had the power. She had struck a magical vein of confidence and cohesion, and was mining it for all she was worth. She was Coco Hernandez. She was going to live forever. When Lydia began speeding up in front of her she accepted the challenge with glee.

The other students stood trans-

fixed by the duelling dancers. Sometimes Coco would move alongside Lydia and give her a radiant, seamless smile. Lydia winked back, but she knew that Coco was hurting, that despite her aggressive, unthinking youthful competitiveness, Coco's lungs were burning, her legs were growing heavy, her heart was pounding. She was hurting all right – Lydia knew because so was she.

"Want to call it a draw?" she hissed.

For a brief second Coco felt a frighteningly powerful urge to go on dancing, to lose herself in the music, to lose Miss Grant, to leave her behind, to go on ahead into the danger zone alone, but something in Lydia's eyes told her she would be making a mistake.

"A draw," she said, coming to a stop as the other pupils indulged in some exaggerated cheering.

Later, after lunch, when Coco was alone, Lydia approached her in the corridor. "There's a Hungarian dance group at the Experimental Theatre on East Fourth Street," she said. "It's not too expensive and I think you might learn something."

"Are you going?" asked Coco.

"No," answered Lydia.

"You wouldn't learn anything if you went?" prodded Coco.

"I've got a previous engagement," Lydia explained.

"Back in the class, I thought we called it a draw."

"We did, Coco. Do I have to beat you every time?"

Coco studied Lydia closely. She did not look her usual radiant self. She looked tired, sick. Maybe the dancing had finally taken its toll. Maybe she had been wrong not to force it. Maybe Lydia was on the slide. If she was, then maybe Coco would be holding back her own development by putting her faith in a teacher who could only teach by words, not example.

"From now on," said Coco quietly, looking Lydia straight in the eyes, "the answer is yes."

Outside the School of the Arts the following morning, Coco was swaying happily from side to side as she watched Leroy go through a routine he had worked out for one of the more reflective tracks from Funkadelic's latest live album on his ghetto blaster. She'd caught the beat, the mood, the feeling.

So had Julie, who was improvising her own private dance behind her. Danny used a rolled up newspaper as a racket in a silent tennis sketch he was working on and Doris sat on the steps studying a tattered copy of *The Misfits*.

An elegant black-haired woman in a tight skirt made her way through the happy, noisy crowd to Coco's side. "Excuse me," she said, "are you Coco Hernandez?"

"Who's asking?"

The woman held out her hand. There was an envelope in it. "Marilyn Beamon. I'm from Costello's Casting. I've got a part you might be interested in. All the information is in here."

Coco had difficulty keeping her mouth closed.

Marilyn smiled. "I've had good reports about you, and you look just right. The auditions are tonight. Be there."

"I'll be there," said Coco.

Marilyn turned and went as the other students came crowding round Coco.

"Girl, you've struck lucky," said Leroy, wistfully shaking his head.

"You'd better not let any of the teachers find out," said Julie.

"They won't know," said Coco, "unless I get the part – and by then I won't care."

"One audition and she's already a star," said Danny. "You won't like Hollywood you know, Coco. Not one of the men is over four feet high. It saves on the sets. And there's the smog –"

"Boy, I will eat smog for breakfast to get there. My time is long overdue. Heck, Brooke Shields had cracked it by the time she was ten years old!"

"What's the part, anyway?" asked Doris, looking at the envelope, but before Coco could open it, Professor Shorofsky appeared, with Lydia and Miss Sherwood.

The crowd dispersed and the day began.

As soon as she could, Coco studied the contents of the envelope. The show for which she would be auditioning was a seventy-five minute pilot TV show about an ex-champion boxer turned sheriff in a small Mississippi town at the turn of the century. The part she was auditioning for was that of Rita, the rebellious daughter of a poor family. The part was small, but it was significant, and in it she was required to do an impromptu dance in a barn.

"What's that you're reading, Coco?" It was Lydia.

"Nothing," said Coco, folding the papers hurriedly into an exercise book and holding it tightly under her arm.

"Have you thought any more about that Hungarian dancing troupe?"

"I've thought about it."

"But you won't be going?"

Coco studied Lydia for any sign that she knew about the audition. If she did know, she was hiding it very well.

"I don't think so," she said.

Coco arrived for the audition right on time. Marilyn was there with Claude Brown, the director, and she told Coco she was on first.

"What do you want me to do?"

"You've read the synopsis?"

Coco nodded.

"Then I want you to do the barn number. I want you to try and express your interpretation of the character through the dance. The girl is alone, remember, so she is totally unselfconscious. The dance expresses her true feelings. OK?"

Coco nodded and went to change. She was so excited she scarcely noticed the familiar figure of Lydia Grant pulling on her practice skirt.

"Hello, Coco."

"So this was your previous appointment?" asked Coco.

"You know you're not meant to be here, girl."

"I know that. But I am here, and I'm going to give it my best shot."

Coco imagined she saw a smile forming on Lydia's face, but before she could be sure Marilyn popped her head round the door and told her she was on.

Once on stage, Coco's nervous-ness was transformed into a marvellous aggression as she attacked the part of Rita with sub-lime confidence. Rita was a rebel? She'd give them rebellion. She knew about rebellion. She knew how it felt watching stars dining out in fur coats when she couldn't afford a hot dog. She knew how it felt to be caught in the poverty trap with no future except to grow old fast and hard faster, while the rest of the world went mad with its bombs and guns and underarm deodorants.

Coco flung herself about the stage like a dervish. So she didn't have money. No shiny cars or swimming pools. She had nothing except her youth, her looks and her talent, and she paraded all three to the full in a virtuoso display. When she finally flopped

down, in time with the music, at the end of her dance, she felt it was just about the best performance she had ever put on.

"Thank you," said a voice from the shadows. "Who's next?"

"Janey Dean," replied Marilyn.

Coco passed a petite blonde on her way offstage.

In the wings, Lydia was waiting to greet her. "That was pretty hot," said Lydia.

"Thanks," said Coco. "Which part are you here for?"

"The same as you."

"Aren't you a bit —"

"Old?" smiled Lydia. "To tell you the truth, I'm feeling that way right now. But the director asked me to come along."

"Why?"

"To help with the choreo-graphy."

"Can you put in a word for me?" asked Coco.

Lydia smiled. "You really want this part, don't you?"

"So bad I can taste it."

"It would probably mean the end of your schooling."

"I'm right for this part. I know it. I can do it."

"And afterwards?"

"I'm talking about now, not yesterday or tomorrow. I'm talking this very minute."

"You'd better watch your step,

girl. Fame ain't no bag of coloured sweets. If you get it before you're ready – and I mean ready, girl – you gonna end up in a nickel and dime grog shop sitting on some punk's knee singing *You Made Me Love You* into his filthy ears."

"Do I look like I just got off the boat? I can do it! I can –"

Coco was interrupted by Marilyn calling Lydia onto the stage. Coco wiped her face with a towel and settled back to watch. She felt cool, calm. She felt that Lydia would have to be at her best to turn in a performance to top the one she'd just given. She felt confident that her teacher couldn't match the pace or power of her own efforts.

But Lydia didn't try to. She danced with the lightness of a child, but her version of Rita was totally different to Coco's. There was grace, there was hope, there was the occasional fire, but Lydia's Rita was no one-dimensional teenager rebelling against authority. Through her dance, Lydia brought to life Rita's fears and insecurities; her whole demeanour suggested a terrible legacy of generations of grinding poverty, dread and fear. Coco remembered Marilyn's advice and she knew at once that Lydia had understood the part of Rita better than she had. Her own performance seemed brash and shallow in comparison. She had only accentuated Rita's ambition and pride and anger. Lydia had suggested all this and more – despair, loneliness, sensitivity, the need to be loved. She had blown it. When Lydia came off, Coco was waiting with a towel.

"You're some dancer," she said.

"You just beginning to find that out?" Lydia smiled. "But I'm too old for the part, remember?"

"You sure didn't dance that way."

"But I am. Coco?" She put her arm on Coco's shoulder and her voice became soft.

"Yes?"

"You could do this part. I know you could make a great success of it . . . with a little coaching. But the next part that comes along might not fit you so well."

"You think I might get it?" asked Coco, brightening.

"I know you won't, girl. Janey Dean will. Didn't I mention her real name is Nina Costello?"

"What?"

"The daughter of the head of the casting agency."

"You knew all the time? You put Marilyn up to it? Why?"

"Why?" repeated Lydia as she and Coco began to change. "You're getting too darned close, and I need to keep on my toes."

"You sure do," laughed Coco. "You surely do."